Helen Orme taught for many years before giving up teaching to write full-time. At the last count she had written over 70 books.

She writes both fiction and non-fiction, but at present is concentrating on fiction for older readers.

Helen also runs writing workshops for children and courses for teachers in both primary and secondary schools.

Don't Let Go

by

Helen Orme

Don't Let Go
by Helen Orme
Illustrated by Chris Askham

Published by Ransom Publishing Ltd.
Radley House, 8 St. Cross Road, Winchester, Hampshire SO23 9HX, UK
www.ransom.co.uk

ISBN 978 184167 153 6
First published in 2013

A CIP catalogue record of this book is available from the British Library.

Siti Musa

Hi! I'm Siti Musa.

Siti is a Swahili (African) name meaning 'Lady'.

I'm the oldest in my family. I have two brothers, Daudi and Hanif, and a kid sister Afia.

My dad is a deputy head at our school, which can be bad news sometimes!

My mum is a social worker.

Lu Clarke

I'm Lu Clarke and I'm an only child. My dad is a businessman – he has an IT office in the town centre. My mum, who is Chinese, works in a bank.

My mum's parents (Po-po and Gong-gong – our name for grandparents) live by the sea. They used to have a Chinese restaurant and my mum worked there when she was younger. My other grandparents live close to us.

My parents want the best for me – but they don't always ask me what *I* want.

Kelly Jonson

I'm Kelly Jonson.

My mum is a single parent. She works as a solicitor. I've got an older brother, Jamie. His girlfriend is Susie.

My parents split when I was very young, and Dad remarried. We don't have any contact with Dad and his new family.

I really want to be a writer – oh, and I fancy Gary! I've decided that I want to be a vegetarian.

Rachel Phillips

I'm Rachel Phillips.

My parents split about 4 years ago. Dad runs a small printing business, and Mum is office manager at our school.

I live with Mum and spend weekends with Dad. His new wife is Janine. They have two young children, a boy and a new baby girl. It's O.K. visiting them, but I'd rather be with Mum.

My older brother Wil is at sixth-form college.

Donna Mills

I'm Donna Mills.

My dad's a bus driver and my mum works in a shop.

I have two older sisters, Marie and Briony. Marie's friend Susie is Kelly's brother's girlfriend.

My brother, Michael, is the youngest.

I love animals and going swimming.

There isn't much spare cash in our family – which makes things hard sometimes.

Chapter 1

'You've got to help me. I can't stand it.'

Now Siti was really worried. This wasn't like Kelly.

'What's wrong?'

'A dog! We've got a dog.'

So that was why Kelly was so upset. Siti knew she hated dogs.

'Come round and tell me about it.'

'I can't. Mum says I've got to stay and look after it.'

'I'll come to yours, then.'

Siti called to her mum.

'I'm going round to Kelly. See you later.'

*****

As Siti got close to Kelly's house she could hear the howling. Kelly opened the door.

'What's going on?' Siti asked.

'I can't stand the thing, so I've shut it in the kitchen,' said Kelly. 'But it doesn't like it.'

'Why have you got a dog anyway?' asked Siti. 'Your mum knows you hate them.'

'Mum's friend Julie had to go into hospital. There wasn't anyone to look after it, so she said she would. What's worse, she says it will be good for me and I've got to help!'

Chapter 2

Siti opened the kitchen door. The dog jumped on her. It was a big, fluffy dog and it was friendly. Very friendly!

She went into the kitchen and pushed the door shut. She knew Kelly would hate it if the dog got out. The dog didn't mind. It was happy now it had someone with it.

'What's its name?' she called.

'Floppy.'

Floppy was a good name for it. It was big and very hairy.

It lay on the floor and rolled over. Siti rubbed its tummy. It loved that.

Siti called to Kelly.

'Open the door and come in. It won't hurt you.'

'No way! I'm not coming in with that thing there.'

'Let's take it for a walk then.'

'Not just us,' Kelly said. 'It's too big. I'm scared.'

'Call the others then.' Siti was getting cross with Kelly. 'Get them to meet us in the park.'

'Where's its lead?' she asked.

‘Here,’ said Kelly.

‘Get it for me then.’

‘But how can I give it to you? If I open the door Floppy will get out.’

‘Come round the back then. You can give it to me through the window.’

Chapter 3

Siti opened the window and grabbed the lead. She tried to put the lead on the dog, but it was hard. He thought she was going to play. He grabbed the end of the lead and shook it hard.

Siti got the lead on and opened the back door. She nearly fell over. Floppy was very strong.

They ran to the park. It was the only way to keep up with Floppy.

The others were already there.

Donna rushed up to them. Floppy jumped up and pushed her over. He pulled his lead out of Siti's hands.

Kelly screamed. 'Get it off her.'

But Donna was laughing. 'He's lovely,' she said.

Kelly looked at Rachel. 'Help her,' she said.

'You know what she's like about animals,' said Rachel. 'She's fine.'

'He's just a puppy,' said Lu. 'He wants to play.'

'We should have brought a ball,' said Siti. 'He would have liked that.'

Kelly was watching Donna hugging Floppy. She picked up a stick.

'He might chase this,' she said.

'Take his lead off then,' said Siti. 'He might get caught up if we leave it on.'

She took the lead off. Floppy stood in front of her, wagging his tail.

He knew this game. He had played it before.

*****

They all had great fun throwing the stick. Even Kelly had a turn. She didn't mind, as long as Floppy didn't jump up.

But then the awful thing happened.

Chapter 4

Siti threw the stick as far as she could – right in front of another dog. A little tiny dog. The little dog got it in his mouth.

Fluffy rushed up and stopped in front of the little dog. He sat down. The little dog dropped the stick. Fluffy went to grab it and the little dog jumped on Floppy.

It grabbed Floppy by the ear and started growling fiercely.

Floppy shook his head, but it wouldn't let go. He started to howl.

The girls ran to help.

'Let him go!' It was Kelly who was in front. She shouted at the little dog.

Suddenly the little dog let go. It grabbed the stick and ran off. Floppy looked at the girls and he started to run too.

But he was running the wrong way. Not to them, but to the park gates.

The girls started to run too. But Floppy was out of the gates.

They heard a screech of car tyres.

'Oh no! No!' yelled Kelly.

Kelly got to the gate first and looked round. It was O.K. Floppy wasn't there.

Siti caught up with her.

'Where is he?'

'He's gone. I can't see him anywhere.'

Chapter 5

The others got to the gate.

'What are we going to do?' asked Lu.

'My mum will kill me,' said Kelly.

'Don't worry, we'll find him,' said Rachel.

Siti took charge.

'We'll go this way,' she told Kelly. 'You three can go the other way.'

Siti and Kelly ran off together.

They looked everywhere. They couldn't find Floppy.

'I'll ring Lu,' said Siti.

‘It’s no good. They would have rung us if they’d found him.’

Then Siti had a really good idea.

‘Where does Julie live?’ she asked. ‘Is it far?’

They soon got to Julie’s house.

They knew they were right even before they got there.

They could hear barking from the end of the road.

Floppy was standing outside the front door.

When he saw Kelly he rushed towards her. Siti tried to get in front of Kelly. She knew what was going to happen.

But, to her surprise, Kelly pushed her away. Kelly flung her arms round Floppy and gave him a big hug.

'I thought you didn't like dogs!' Siti said.

'I don't,' said Kelly, 'but, for a dog, Floppy's not too bad after all.'

Siti's Sisters
The early years

– one year on:
the Sisters
are older

– another year on:
The Sisters have grown up (well, nearly ...)